This book belongs to...

Daisydaisy

DISNEY ANNUAL 1995

CONTENTS

Origination by
Original Thoughts (Aylesbury).

MICKEY & GOOFY

THE HAUNTED LIGHTHOUSE

LAND'S END LIGHTHOUSE, EH? LOOKS LIKE A MIGHTY BIG *TORCH* TO ME, CHIEF.

IT'S NOT JUST *ANY* LIGHTHOUSE, GOOFY. MY BROTHER, CAP'N O'HARA LIVES THERE AND I'M WORRIED ABOUT HIM.

WHAT'S THE PROBLEM?

D92092

HE KEEPS RINGING ME WITH TALES OF WEIRD SIGHTS AND SOUNDS IN THE MIDDLE OF THE NIGHT.

IT'S NOT LIKE HIM— HE'S AN OLD *SEA DOG!* SEEN IT ALL, DONE IT ALL, NOT EASILY SPOOKED.

CAN YOU CHECK UP ON HIM, BOYS? I'D HATE TO THINK HE WAS LOSING HIS MARBLES OUT THERE.

HEY, WHY DON'T *YOU* COME TOO, CHIEF?

I WISH I COULD, MICKEY, BUT I'M BUSY LOOKING FOR THIS GUY...

HECTOR HENNESSY, THE FAMOUS *TREASURE HUNTER!* HE'S GONE MISSING, HAS HE?

GOT ANY LEADS?

NOTHING! THAT'S WHY I CAN'T JUST DROP EVERYTHING AND COME WITH YOU!

5

SHORTLY...

I SURE HOPE CHIEF O'HARA'S BROTHER IS OKAY, EH, GOOFY?

CHOMP!

GREEDY GANNET! YOU HAVEN'T STOPPED EATING SINCE WE LEFT DUCKBURG!

SHUCKS, MICKEY, *SEA AIR* ALWAYS MAKES ME HUNGRY!

BUT WE'RE NOWHERE NEAR THE SEA YET!

I KNOW, I'M JUST FILLING UP IN *ADVANCE*, THAT'S ALL!

(SIGH!) CHECK THE MAP, GOOFY. I'M NOT SURE WE'RE ON THE RIGHT ROAD.

OKEY-DOKE! WE'VE JUST PASSED...ER... *RED BLOB!*

AND WE'LL SOON SEE THE NEXT RED BLOB...

RED BLOBS? WHAT ARE YOU TALKING ABOUT, GOOFY?

SCREECH!

YOU'VE SPLATTERED THE MAP WITH TOMATO KETCHUP! IT'S RUINED!

GAWRSH! IT TASTES OKAY TO ME!

LATER...

OH GREAT! WE'RE COMPLETELY LOST!

NO, WE'RE NOT, MICKEY. WE JUST DON'T KNOW WHERE WE ARE!

113

6

SOON...

I MIGHT AS WELL HAVE BEEN DRIVING *BLINDFOLD!* YOU AND YOUR KETCHUP!

I'LL BRING ALONG SOME *PEA SOUP* NEXT TIME, THEN I'LL BE ABLE TO MARK ALL THIS FOG ON THE MAP.

HEY, MICKEY! I THINK I'VE FOUND A *ROAD SIGN* HERE.

ABOUT TIME— *COME ON!*

IF WE STAY ON THIS ROAD WE SHOULD BE ALL RIGHT.

LET'S HOPE WE CAN *SEE* IT LONG ENOUGH TO STAY ON IT UNTIL WE GET TO THE LIGHTHOUSE.

D'YOU THINK THE LIGHT-HOUSE MIGHT BE A *BELL*HOUSE, TOO?

WHAT'S THAT? A BELL?

DONG! DING! DONG!

DONG! DONG!

G-GAAWRRSH!

IT'S A GHOSTLY GALLEON!

IT'S A G-GOOD JOB W-WE'RE N-NOT EASILY S-SCARED, ISN'T IT, M-MICKEY?

SURE IS, GOOFY! AT LEAST WE'VE ARRIVED AT LAST – I THINK I CAN SEE THE *LIGHTHOUSE* THROUGH THE FOG.

AND SO...

W-WHO'S THERE..? OH, YOU MUST BE MICKEY AND GOOFY!

YOU JUST MISSED THE GHOST SHIP I'VE BEEN TELLING MY BROTHER ABOUT...

NO, WE *DIDN'T!* WE SAW IT ALL RIGHT AND IT SCARED US HALF TO DEATH!

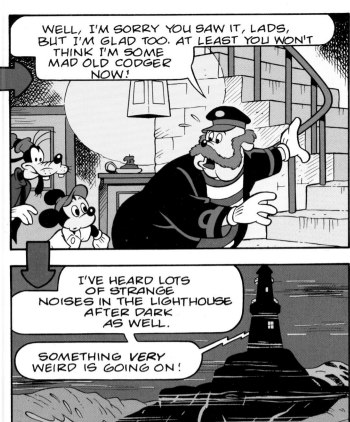

WELL, I'M SORRY YOU SAW IT, LADS, BUT I'M GLAD TOO. AT LEAST YOU WON'T THINK I'M SOME MAD OLD CODGER NOW!

I'VE HEARD LOTS OF STRANGE NOISES IN THE LIGHTHOUSE AFTER DARK AS WELL.

SOMETHING *VERY* WEIRD IS GOING ON!

WHY DON'T YOU TELL US ABOUT IT IN THE MORNING, CAP'N? WE COULD ALL DO WITH A GOOD NIGHT'S SLEEP AFTER THAT FRIGHT.

YAWN! GOOD IDEA!

OF COURSE. MAKE YOURSELVES AT HOME, LADS. AND DON'T FORGET TO TURN THE LIGHT OFF! *HEE HEE!*

SHORTLY...

GOLLY! ALL THAT EATING'S MADE ME SLEEPY!

HA, HA! NIGHT, GOOFY!

URHH! WHAT'S THAT NOISE?

D'YOU THINK *PLUTO'S* FOLLOWED US HERE?

SCRRRP! SCRTTT!

DID YOU HEAR IT?

YES, WHERE'S IT COMING FROM?

SCRRRP!

FROM THE *BASEMENT!*

LET'S GET DOWN THERE AND TAKE A LOOK!

SCRRP!

SO...

THERE IT GOES AGAIN!

SCRRRP! SCRRPP!

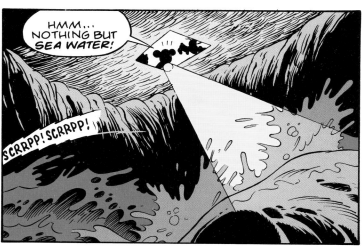

HMM... NOTHING BUT *SEA WATER!*

SCRRPP! SCRRPP!

DOESN'T SEEM TO BE ANYTHING STRANGE DOWN THERE, CAP'N, NOT UNLESS THE *INVISIBLE MAN'S* OUT FOR A SWIM!

SCRRRT! SCRRRT!

IT'S FUNNY, THOUGH. I'VE BEEN HERE YEARS, BUT I'VE ONLY JUST STARTED HEARING THESE NOISES.

WELL, IT SURE SEEMS TO BE THE WIND BLOWING AMONG THE ROCKS, BUT IT DOES SEEM MIGHTY *SUSPICIOUS.*

MORNING...

THIS COAST USED TO BE A BIG SMUGGLING AREA, BOYS. THIS OLD CANNON'S A REMINDER OF THE OLDEN DAYS!

GEE, THAT'S QUITE A *PEA-SHOOTER,* CAP'N!

LET'S TAKE A LOOK AROUND THE BEACH. COME ON!

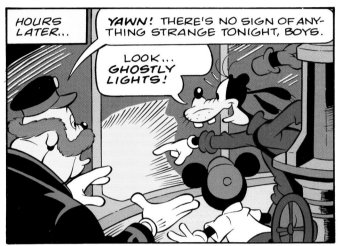

THE GHOSTLY GOINGS ON CONTINUE ON PAGE 13!...

SNOW JOKE!

Brrr! Donald Duck, his nephews, Daisy and Uncle Scrooge are all on a visit to the **Antarctic**, but there are some rather strange things about this picture. Can you spot **eight** things which you would not really expect to find in the Antarctic?

THE STORY SO FAR:

CHIEF O'HARA'S BROTHER, CAP'N O'HARA HAS BEEN THE KEEPER OF LAND'S END LIGHTHOUSE FOR MANY YEARS. RECENTLY HE HAS BEEN HEARING SOME VERY STRANGE NOISES COMING FROM THE BASEMENT, IN THE MIDDLE OF THE NIGHT SO MICKEY MOUSE AND GOOFY HAVE COME DOWN TO INVESTIGATE. NOW A GHOSTLY GALLEON IS ON A COLLISION COURSE WITH THE LIGHTHOUSE...

SHE ISN'T STOPPING! SHE'LL BE SMASHED TO BITS!

DON'T THEY HAVE BRAKES?

BUT IF SHE'S REALLY A GHOST SHIP, SHE WON'T CRASH- SHE'LL PASS RIGHT THROUGH THE LIGHTHOUSE!

YOU MEAN SHE'LL BE COMING IN HERE? WITH LOTS OF GHOSTS ABOARD HER?

THE FOG'S COMING DOWN!

SHE'LL HIT ANY MOMENT!

I CAN'T LOOK! HOLD ONTO YOUR HATS!

BUT...

UH? IT'S VANISHED!

SO HAS THE FOG!

SO WHAT HAPPENED?

BEATS ME!

14

SPLUTTER! FOR A GHOST SHIP, THIS IS MIGHTY **SOLID**!

PUFF! IF I CAN JUST **ANCHOR** MYSELF ON HERE...

GAWRSH! SO THIS IS WHERE THE GALLEON DISAPPEARED TO BEFORE— INTO THE CLIFF!

AND THE DOOR CLOSES RIGHT BEHIND IT. **NEAT!**

SOON...

THAT PRISONER LOOKS **FAMILIAR**...

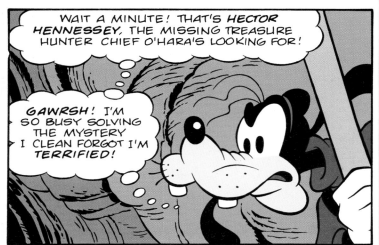

WAIT A MINUTE! THAT'S **HECTOR HENNESSEY**, THE MISSING TREASURE HUNTER CHIEF O'HARA'S LOOKING FOR!

GAWRSH! I'M SO BUSY SOLVING THE MYSTERY I CLEAN FORGOT I'M **TERRIFIED**!

WELL, WE'RE THROUGH LOOTING **THE UNSINKABLE** - THANKS TO OUR FRIEND HECTOR, HERE!

PRETTY KIND OF HIM TO HELP US, DON'T YOU THINK?

THAT **FLUORESCENT PAINT** WORKED WELL ON THE "GHOST SHIP", TOO, EH?

YEAH, IT KEPT AWAY THE NOSEY PARKERS WHILE WE GOT THE TREASURE!

WHOOPS!

SPLASH!

AN INTRUDER!

UH-OH!

MEANWHILE—

GOOFY! WHERE ARE YOU?

LOOK!

THE ROWING BOAT'S WRECKED!

OMIGOSH! POOR GOOFY.

DAWN...

SO LONG, SUCKERS! HAVE FUN AS THE TIDE COMES IN!

YOU'LL PAY FOR THIS, YOU SCOUNDRELS!

WE COULD PAY FOR PRETTY MUCH **ANYTHING** WITH ALL THIS TREASURE, PAL!

SHORTLY...

MY OLD PAL! (**SOB!**) I CAN'T BELIEVE HE'S...

MICKEY! I CAN HEAR SOMEONE!

IT'S **GOOFY!** COME ON, CAP'N!

HULLLPP!

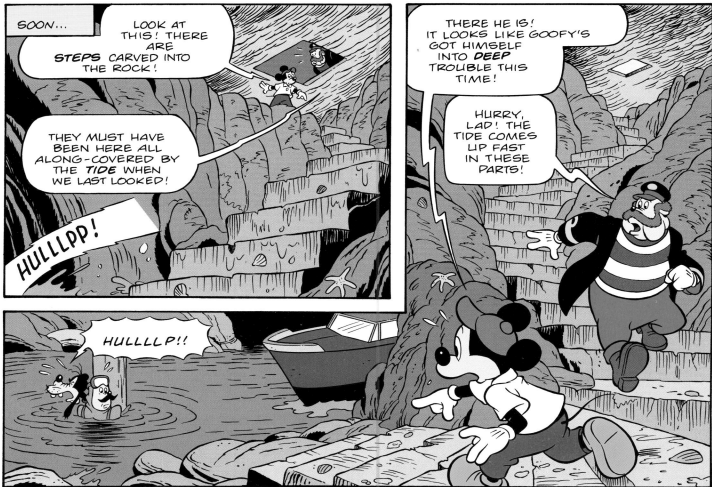

SOON... LOOK AT THIS! THERE ARE **STEPS** CARVED INTO THE ROCK!

THEY MUST HAVE BEEN HERE ALL ALONG—COVERED BY THE **TIDE** WHEN WE LAST LOOKED!

HULLLPP!

THERE HE IS! IT LOOKS LIKE GOOFY'S GOT HIMSELF INTO **DEEP** TROUBLE THIS TIME!

HURRY, LAD! THE TIDE COMES UP FAST IN THESE PARTS!

HULLLLP!!

GAWRSH! YOU FOUND US! I THOUGHT WE WUZ **GONERS!**

LET'S GET YOU OUT OF HERE, THEN YOU CAN TELL US **EXACTLY** WHAT'S BEEN GOING ON.

SOON... WE'LL GO AFTER THEM IN THIS **SPEEDBOAT!**

OKAY! WE'LL CALL THE **COASTGUARD!**

18

20

THE END.

BEAU DUCK

24

25

500 HOT AND DUSTY KILOMETRES LATER...

TAKE THE WHEEL WHILE I HAVE A NAP.

WHICH WAY?

STRAIGHT AHEAD, OF COURSE, JUST LIKE THE LAST 500 KM!

LET ME SEE NOW... DAISY... DAISY WHO? SEE, I'VE FORGOTTEN HER ALREADY!

GEE, THE PEOPLE DRESS DIFFERENTLY WAY OUT HERE!

ALL YOU CAN SEE OF THAT GIRL ARE A PAIR OF EYES!

THEY'RE NOT AS PRETTY AS DAISY'S, THOUGH. SIGH!

I DID BRING A TINY PICTURE OF HER...

I'LL BE ABLE TO SEE IT BETTER WITH THE MAP-READING MAGNIFYING GLASS! WHERE IS IT?

WILL DONALD FORGET? WILL HE EVER GET DOWN FROM THAT TREE? FIND OUT IN PART 2 OF THIS STORY BEGINNING ON PAGE 30!

DOTS IN THE SLOT!

Mickey Mouse's nephews, Morty and Ferdy are keen to put their money in this slot because they think what they can see is very funny! Can you guess who or what it is? Sharpen your pencil and carefully join all these dots to find out!

PHEW! THEY'VE GONE! IF THEY'D FOUND ME, I THINK I'D HAVE BEEN *DUCK KEBAB* BY NOW!

THE STORY SO FAR:
HAVING SEEN DAISY DECLARE HER LOVE FOR ACTOR VICTOR MELDRAKE, DONALD DUCK DECIDED TO THROW IN HIS JOB AS A HAMBURGER CHEF AND TRAVEL THE WORLD IN A EFFORT TO FORGET HIS ONE TRUE LOVE. AFTER A DISASTROUS SPELL AS A SAILOR, HE GOT A JOB DRIVING A CONVOY ACROSS THE DESERT, HOWEVER, WHEN HE DROVE INTO A PALM TREE HE HAD TO HIDE FROM THE OTHER ANGRY DRIVERS! NOW THEY'RE GONE AND HE'S ON HIS OWN IN THE DESERT... OR IS HE?

D93071

OKAY, SO I SURVIVED- BUT HOW LONG BEFORE I'M A *ROAST DUCK* IN THIS HEAT ANYWAY?

I'LL JUST HAVE TO FOLLOW THESE TRACKS. IT'S ONLY *4500 KILOMETRES* TO SAND CITY...

HELLO, UNCA DONALD!

WAAKKK!

IT CAN'T BE! YOU'RE A *MIRAGE!*

OOF! NO, WE'RE NOT!

WE'VE BEEN FOLLOWING YOU, UNCA...

...WE STOWED AWAY ON THE SHIP...

...AND THEN WE HID IN THE BACK OF A TRUCK!

THANKS FOR YOUR CONCERN, BOYS, BUT THIS IS SOMETHING I HAVE TO DO *ALONE!*

BUT WE'RE LOST IN THE DESERT, TOO, NOW...

WE NEED YOU TO HELP US FIND OUR WAY HOME!

ALL RIGHT, THEN! LET'S TRY THIS WAY – WE MUST BUMP INTO **SOMETHING** SOONER OR LATER!

LATER, RATHER THAN SOONER...

AT LAST! AN OLD *FORT!*

I HOPE THERE'S SOMEONE AT HOME AFTER WE CAME ALL THIS WAY!

IT'S THE *FOREIGN LEGION!* WHAT LUCK!

JUST THE PLACE FOR A **BROKEN-HEARTED** DUCK TO FORGET HIS PAST!

31

BLAM! BLAM!

WAK!

I SURRENDER! DON'T SHOOT ME!

HEE, HEE!

THIS AIN'T NO *DUCK SHOOT!* YOU'RE IN THE WAY OF OUR *TARGET PRACTICE!*

OH!

ER, WELL...I'M *CADET D. DUCK* READY TO SIGN UP FOR THE *FOREIGN LEGION!*

SORRY, THE LEGION LEFT HERE *60 YEARS AGO!* WE MOVED IN AFTER, WE'RE THE *DESERT RANGERS!*

I WANT TO JOIN ANYWAY!

WHAT FOR? DID YOU *MURDER* SOMEONE, OR ROB A BANK?

NO, ER... I GOT *GIRL TROUBLE!*

OH, YEAH?

HELLO, WHAT'S THIS? DID YOU BRING ALONG YOUR *FAN CLUB?*

34

WE'RE FROM DUCKBURG! WE WATCH *DB-TV* ALL THE TIME!

REALLY? LET ME SHOW YOU SOMETHING...

WE CAN PICK UP DUCKBURG SHOWS WITH OUR *SATELLITE DISH*! WANNA TAKE A LOOK?

YES, PLEASE!

HOPE IT'S MY FAVOURITE—*THE BURGER SHOW!*

AND NOW THE WINNING PLAY IN THE DB-TV *DRAMA* CONTEST...

..."FORBIDDEN PASSION" STARS ACTOR VICTOR MEL-DRAKE AND TALENTED NEW-COMER, DAISY DUCK!

DO YOU KNOW JUST HOW MUCH I LOVE YOU?

YES, BUT YOU BELONG TO SOME ONE ELSE!

A *PLAY*? BUT THAT'S WHAT SHE SAID WHEN I HEARD HER — *WAK!*

I GOTTA TALK TO HER RIGHT AWAY!

PERHAPS I CAN HELP?

MOMENTS LATER...

DAISY? IS THAT YOU?

DONALD! WHERE *HAVE* YOU BEEN? I'VE BEEN *WORRIED!*

THE END

ESCAPE FROM DING DING!

PANIC OVER, BOYS! WHY **SWIM** TO DING DING WHEN WE CAN TAKE YOU IN THE BOAT?

GROAN!

I THINK I'LL GO **BELOW DECK.** MAYBE THE SEA'S NOT SO **ROUGH** DOWN THERE! MY POOR **HEAD...**

GOING TO PRISON IS JUST NO FUN AT ALL!

SHORTLY...

JUMP IN THE BACK OF THE VAN, BOYS! YOUR VISIT TO THE PRISON IS **TOP SECRET!** YOU MUSTN'T BE SEEN!

WHAT'S THAT AWFUL **SMELL?** I FEEL SICK ENOUGH ALREADY!

THIS IS THE **PIG SWILL** VAN. IT'S THE BEST COVER FOR SNEAKING YOU INTO DING DING!

SOON...

SORRY ABOUT THE VAN, BUT IT'S IMPORTANT NO-ONE KNOWS YOU'RE HERE TO INVESTIGATE WHAT'S GOING ON AT THE PRISON.

YOU SMELL A **RAT,** EH? CAN'T BE ANY WORSE THAN THAT **PIG SWILL!**

AS YOU KNOW, DING DING PRISON IS **ESCAPE-PROOF!** NO-ONE HAS **EVER** ESCAPED FROM HERE!

JUST AS I THOUGHT. THAT **CROSSING** WOULD CERTAINLY PUT **ME** OFF AS WELL!

SO WHAT'S THE PROBLEM, GOVERNOR?

WELL, A PRISONER **HAS** FINALLY ESCAPED! **YESTERDAY!** AND WE DON'T KNOW **HOW!**

SURELY YOU HAVE **SOME** IDEA. WHAT ABOUT ALL YOUR **SECURITY**?

WELL, THE PRISON'S SURROUNDED BY DANGEROUS WATERS AND THERE ARE COUNTLESS GUARDS ALL OVER THE PLACE...

...PLUS, WE HAVE AN ELECTRONIC **MAXIMUM SECURITY SYSTEM** AND NOTHING'S BEEN DISTURBED, BROKEN OR TAMPERED WITH!

THE **POLICE** AND **COASTGUARDS** HAVE BEEN NOTIFIED, BUT THEY'VE NOT COME UP WITH ANYTHING, EITHER!

IF WE DON'T FIND THE ESCAPE ROUTE QUICKLY WE'RE LIKELY TO HAVE A **MASS BREAKOUT** ON OUR HANDS BEFORE LONG!

QUITE A PROBLEM...

THERE'S **ANOTHER** PROBLEM! WE HAVE A **REPORTER** HERE. HE WAS DOING A STORY ON THE PRISON WHEN THE ESCAPE HAPPENED!

HE WANTS TO PRINT THE STORY OF THE ESCAPE, BUT HE'S AGREED TO GIVE US A BIT MORE TIME BEFORE BREAKING THE NEWS!

I WANT YOU BOYS TO GO INSIDE THE PRISON AS **PRISONERS** TO TRY TO SOLVE THIS MYSTERY!

WHAT? WITH ALL THE **VILLAINS** YOU'VE GOT IN THERE?

IT'S WORTH A TRY, GOOFY! IT'S OUR BEST CHANCE OF FINDING OUT IF ANY-ONE ELSE IS PLANNING AN ESCAPE.

AW, DO WE HAVE TO, MICKEY? I DON'T KNOW IF I'D LIKE **PRISON FOOD**!

JUST THEN...

LISTEN, I'M TIRED OF HANGING ABOUT! CAN ANYONE TELL ME WHAT'S GOING ON?

WELL, ER... WE WERE JUST TALKING ABOUT **FOOD**...

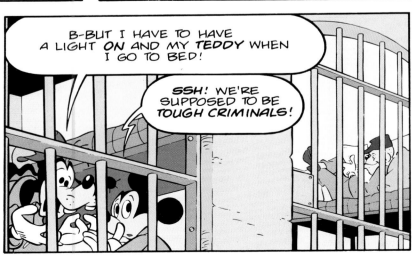

42

BUT THEN...

HELP!

CLICK!

OHHH! I DON'T LIKE THE *DARK!*

CALM DOWN, GOOFY! WE HAVE TO BE ALERT, THIS IS THE BEST TIME FOR US TO LISTEN OUT FOR *CLUES!*

AND...

36!

HA! HA! HA! HA! HA!

HA! HA! HA! HA!

HUH? WHAT'S SO FUNNY?

BEATS ME!

210!

HA! HA! HA! HA! HA! HA!

HO! HO! THIS LAUGHTER'S CATCHING! HA! HA! HA!

AT LEAST IT'S CHEERED YOU UP A BIT AND STOPPED YOU *PANICKING!*

99!

OHH! HO, HO, HEE, HEE!

HA! HA! HA! HA! HA!

WHAT'S SO FUNNY ABOUT *NUMBERS?*

DUNNO, BUT I'M GONNA TRY ONE...

112!

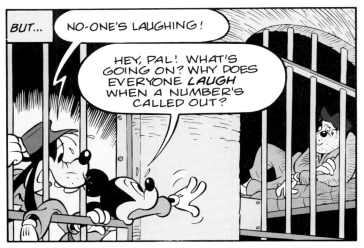

SMELLS LIKE TROUBLE IN DING DING – MICKEY'S JAILHOUSE BLUES CONTINUE ON
PAGE 46!

BEWARE OF THE CROCODILE!

Sometimes you just can't go out for a quiet boat trip on the river without running into a load of bad-tempered large-toothed lizards, can you?

Can you spot ten differences between these two pictures A and B?

ANSWERS:

THE STORY SO FAR:
A DANGEROUS PRISONER HAS ESCAPED FROM THE **ESCAPE-PROOF** DING DING JAIL AND MICKEY AND GOOFY HAVE 24 HOURS TO FIND OUT HOW HE DID IT BEFORE A JOURNALIST PUBLISHES NEWS OF THE ESCAPE. POSING AS PRISONERS, THEY ARE PUT IN THE CELLS, THEN MICKEY HEARS A **HISSING** SOUND...

SMELLS LIKE **GAS!** GOOFY'S OUT ALREADY AND I CAN HARDLY KEEP MY EYES OPEN!

SNORE!

HISSSS!

I'LL HOLD THIS **BLANKET** OVER MY MOUTH AND TRY NOT TO BREATHE!

SURELY THEY DON'T GAS THE PRISONERS EVERY NIGHT TO KEEP THEM QUIET!

OR PERHAPS THEY DO! ALL THESE **HARD MEN** SEEM TO BE SLEEPING LIKE **BABIES** NOW!

ZZZZZZZ!

BUT THEN...

SOMEONE'S MOVING IN THE NEXT CELL!

47

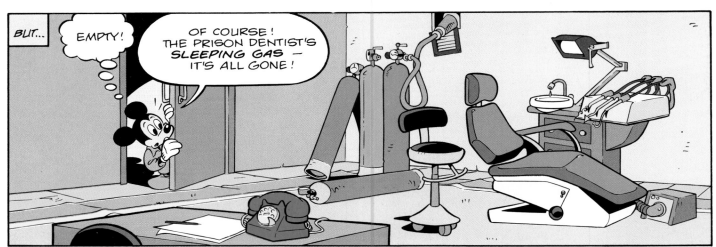

48

FUNNY PLACE FOR A MOLE!

THPP! THPP!

SOME KIND OF TUNNEL... *IS* THERE ANYONE DOWN THERE?

MMFFF!

YOU SURE AIN'T THE *LONE RANGER!*

MMFFF!

AND...

EH? YOU'RE THAT REPORTER! WHAT ARE YOU DOING HERE?

I WAS DOING MY STORY WHEN ONE OF THE PRISONERS ASKED TO SEE ME PRIVATELY – SAID HE HAD AN *EXCLUSIVE* FOR ME!

I WAS DUPED! HE OVERPOWERED ME AND NICKED MY CLOTHES, THEN HE DUMPED ME DOWN THERE!

WELL, AT LEAST YOU GOT TO THE *BOTTOM OF THINGS* – THE BOTTOM OF A *TUNNEL* TO BE EXACT! PRETTY EXCLUSIVE, EH?

SEEMS HE'S A *MASTER OF DISGUISE,* TOO. HE OBVIOUSLY HAD NO TROUBLE IMPERSONATING *ME* IN THE PRISON!

SO THERE NEVER *WAS* AN ESCAPE! HE'S STILL HERE!

HE AND HIS GANG MUST HAVE PLANNED THE ESCAPE – AND THAT TUNNEL – AGES AGO!

YES, AND DISGUISING HIMSELF AS ME MUST HAVE BEEN A GREAT HELP, SINCE IT WILL HAVE GIVEN HIM ACCESS TO THE WHOLE PRISON!

SO HE'LL BE GETTING HIS GANG TOGETHER RIGHT NOW! THEY'LL BE READY TO START THEIR ESCAPE ANY MOMENT!

NOT *ANY* MOMENT—*THIS* MOMENT!

ULP!

QUICK! THE *PHONE*!

STOP HIM!

HAH!

SMASH!

WELL, THIS IS A BETTER STORY THAN ANY YOU WERE WRITING, MATE! THOUGH YOU DID HELP US WRITE A *HAPPY ENDING!*

IT WAS GOOD OF YOU TO TEST OUR TUNNEL FOR US, TOO. I HOPE YOU ENJOYED YOUR STAY!

TALKING OF WHICH—IT'S TIME TO END *OUR* STAY HERE! COME ON, BOYS, THROUGH THE TUNNEL TO OUR WAITING BOAT!

BUT FIRST, I'LL JUST TIE UP THESE TWO *LOOSE ENDS...*

SUDDENLY—

ZZZZZ

OOFFF!

CRASSH!

CAN I HAVE A GLASS OF WATER, MOM?

UH?

HANDS UP! YOU'RE GOING *NOWHERE!*

ZZZZZ

WHAT HIT ME?

YOU'RE *LUCKY* YOU DIDN'T ESCAPE. YOU WOULDN'T HAVE LASTED LONG AS VILLAINS IN THE OUTSIDE WORLD ANYWAY!

WHAT D'YA MEAN?

ZZZZZ

HERE'S THE PROOF! THERE ARE GUYS OUT THERE WHO CAN BEAT YOU WITH THEIR EYES CLOSED! *HA, HA!*

BAH!

BEFORE LONG...

WELL, THEY'RE ALL *BACK BEHIND BARS* NOW!

AND SO ARE THEIR *ACCOMPLICES!* THAT'S THE KIND OF *JAILBREAK* I LIKE!

WHAT A STORY! WHEN GOOFY WAKES UP I'LL GET AN EXCLUSIVE FROM BOTH OF YOU!

51

LATER... WELL DONE, BOYS! AND, SINCE NO-ONE ACTUALLY ESCAPED, DING DING CAN STILL CLAIM TO BE *ESCAPE-PROOF!*

ALL THANKS TO THE *SLEEPING DETECTIVE!*

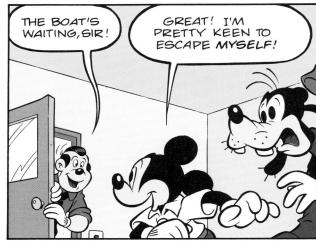

THE BOAT'S WAITING, SIR!

GREAT! I'M PRETTY KEEN TO ESCAPE MYSELF!

BUT... WHERE'S GOOFY?

HE WAS HERE A MINUTE AGO!

MUCH LATER... WE'VE SEARCHED EVERYWHERE, SIR. HE'S *VANISHED!*

LOOKS LIKE ANOTHER MYSTERY FOR YOU TO SOLVE, MICKEY!

HMM... MAYBE THE SOLUTION TO THIS ONE LIES IN THE SAME PLACE AS THE LAST ONE!

I THOUGHT SO! COME OUT, GOOFY! YOU DON'T WANT TO SPEND THE REST OF YOUR LIFE IN *DING DING,* DO YOU?

I CAN'T DO IT! I FEEL *SEASICK* ALREADY!

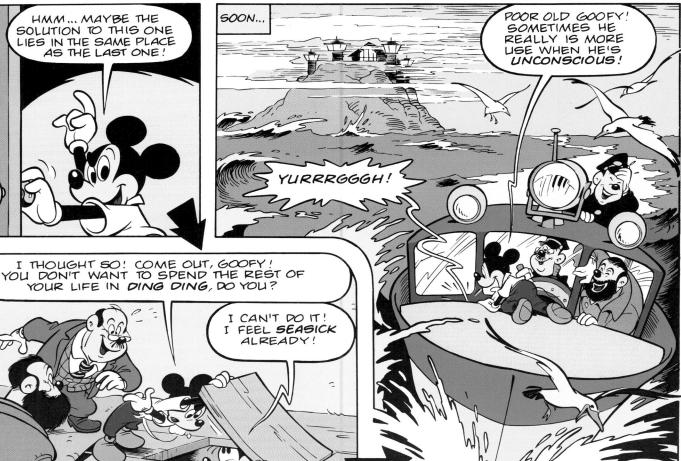

SOON...

POOR OLD GOOFY! SOMETIMES HE REALLY IS MORE USE WHEN HE'S *UNCONSCIOUS!*

YURRRGGGH!

THE END

DONALD DUCK

FOR THE CHOP!

FROM UP OLD **SAWTOOTH MOUNTAIN?**

YEP! THERE'S OODLES OF TREES UP THERE JUST CRYING OUT TO BE HAULED HOME - AND THEY ARE ALL **FREE!**

WELL, HE SOUNDS **CONFIDENT...**

...BUT DOESN'T HE **ALWAYS...**

...AND THINGS STILL SEEM TO END UP IN **DISASTER** MOST OF THE TIME! ULP!

MEANWHILE, DONALD'S NEIGHBOUR, **MISTER JONES** IS HAVING THE SAME TROUBLE...

TOO **PUNY!**

£9.99

TOO BIG! TOO SMALL! TOO EXPENSIVE! THIS IS A REGULAR **BOTANICAL REJECT** SHOP!

GOT A PROBLEM, BUDDY?

YEAH! I CAME HERE TO BUY A CHRISTMAS TREE AND ALL YOU'VE GOT IS A SAD COLLECTION OF **TOOTHPICKS** AND **TOILET BRUSHES!** I WOULDN'T GIVE 'EM HOUSEROOM!

IF THAT'S HOW YOU FEEL, WHY DON'T YA GO AND CUT DOWN ONE OF YER OWN!

HMM...

FREE

RIGHT THEN! LET'S SEE IF THAT **GUY'S ADVICE** IS ANY BETTER THAN HIS **MANKY** TREES! HUR, HUR!

'ONEST 'ARRY

UP THE MOUNTAIN, DONALD AND THE BOYS HEAD FOR THE TALL TIMBER...

AH, THIS IS THE ONLY WAY TO GET A CHRISTMAS TREE! FRESH AIR! EXERCISE! THE WOODSMAN ON THE TRACK OF HIS PREY!

HOW COME THE WOODSMAN DOESN'T CARRY HIS OWN AXE?

I HAVE TO BE FREE TO THINK! WE DON'T WANT TO PICK ANY OLD TREE, DO WE?

AND THE CHOICE IS BIG...

LET'S GET A 15 FOOT TREE, UNCA!

NO! CUT A 20 FOOTER!

PAH! WHY SETTLE FOR A SMALL TREE? LET'S HAVE A 30 FOOTER!

HANG ON, BOYS! WE'RE LOOKING FOR A CHRISTMAS TREE — WE'RE NOT OPENING A TIMBER YARD!

NOW SPREAD OUT — LET'S FIND THE PERFECT TREE!

OKAY, BOSS! ONE PERFECT TREE COMING UP!

ONCE AGAIN, HOWEVER, THE PERFECT TREE IS HARD TO FIND...

TOO SKINNY!

TOO FAT!

TOO SILLY!

HEY! I THINK I CAN SEE JUST WHAT WE'RE LOOKING FOR!

HAVE I GOT A GREAT WOODSMAN'S EYE, OR WHAT? THIS REALLY IS THE *IDEAL* CHRISTMAS TREE!

SHAKE THE SNOW OFF IT, DEWEY, AND WE'LL TAKE A LOOK!

FLUMP!

I THINK THE 'GREAT WOODSMAN' NEEDS GLASSES!

HA! HA! HA!

SURE IS THE IDEAL TREE... *NOT!*

ALL RIGHT, WISE GUYS! THERE ARE *OTHER* FISH IN THE SEA!

YEAH, BUT WE'RE UP A *MOUNTAIN!*

LOOK! THAT REALLY *IS* THE PERFECT TREE!

AMAZING! HOW DID WE MISS THAT?

IT'S *BEAUTIFUL!*

AND BEST OF ALL... IT'S *OURS!*

GRR! YOU COULDN'T STAND TO SEE ME WITH A NIFTY LITTLE TREE, EH, DUCK? YOU JUST *HAD* TO MESS IT UP!

B-BUT IT WAS AN *ACCIDENT,* JONESY, HONEST!

ACCIDENT!?! I'LL GIVE *YOU* AN ACCIDENT, YOU DEMENTED DUCK! THIS MEANS *WAR!*

RUN! HE'S GONE *BERSERK!*

A HASTY RETREAT LATER...

THIS ONE WON'T WIN ANY *BEST TREE* AWARDS, BUT AT LEAST IT'S NICE AND *BUSHY!*

LET'S GET IT HOME BEFORE JONES SHOWS UP!

TOO LATE, CHUMP! LET'S SEE HOW YOUR PRETTY LITTLE TREE STANDS UP TO A *HURRICANE!*

WIND MACHINE

WHOOSH!

OUR TREE!

IT'S AS *BALD* AS A COOT!

DON'T WORRY... IT'LL MAKE A LOVELY *MATCHSTICK,* DUCK!

SOON...

AHA! PERFECTION AT LAST! A TREE THAT'S AS WELL-SHAPED AND UP-STANDING AS I AM, MYSELF!

SMUSH!

NOT ANY MORE IT ISN'T! NOW IT'S *FLATTER* THAN YOUR HEAD! *HA! HA! HA!*

!

59

HA, HA! 10 OUT OF 10 FOR EFFORT, JONESY - BUT A BIG, FAT *ZERO* FOR TECHNICAL MERIT!

LATER...

LISTEN, BOYS! I'VE GOT A *CUNNING PLAN* TO STOP JONES *SABOTAGING* OUR NEXT TREE!

SHALL WE TIE HIM TO A BIG TREE?

NOPE! WE'LL SPREAD OUT AND EACH GET A TREE. WE'LL HAVE TO PASS THE AXE AROUND, BUT JONES CAN'T CATCH US *ALL*!

OH, NO? WE'LL SEE ABOUT THAT! *HUR, HUR!*

SO...

WE'VE EACH GOT A TREE, UNCA DONALD!

NOW WHAT?

STAY SPREAD OUT! EVEN JONES CAN'T BE IN FOUR PLACES AT ONCE!

GUESS AGAIN, BANANA-BEAK!

RUMBLE!

WAK! HE'S STARTED AN *AVALANCHE!*

YIKES! QUICK, *RUN!*

WHAT ABOUT OUR TREES?

FORGET THE SILLY TREES AND RUN FOR COVER, BOYS!